Cool Cat

Written by Judy Cooper
Illustrated by Mike Walsh

Content Strand: Physical Science
Focus: Colors

Cool Cat has a red hat.

Cool Cat has green pants.

Cool Cat has blue shoes.

Cool Cat has a yellow tie.

Cool Cat has orange rings.

Cool Cat has pink glasses.

Cool Cat has a cool car.